Empowered Though Disabled

Accepting Responsibilities as a Disabled Person

Susan P. Clark

SUSAN P. CLARK

ISBN: 978-1-916770-57-7

Dedication

*To **you**, as life has thrown you a nasty curve ball.*

Acknowledgments

My Son, Scott Allen Denny, for lovingly and fearfully watching me go through everything from the start.

My Mom, Patsy Sue Clark, who doesn't handle helpless well but has always been here for me.

My brother and sister-in-love, Russ and Judy Clark, for their quiet, strong support, love and respect throughout.

My Counselor Anita Erickson, for her kindly harsh guidance all these years.

To Tom & Betty Williams and Greg & Heidi Herbruck, who made publishing a reality.

Contents

About the Author

Susan Clark is a professional writer, speaker, and comedian. She loves words and uses their power to encourage readers and listeners alike.

She was diagnosed with Multiple Sclerosis (MS) in 2002, but the search for her physical challenges began in 1978. A neurologist tested her for MS in 1992 without a definitive diagnosis. The disease fully disabled her in 2011. In addition to MS, Susan has survived two bouts with a rare Ovarian cancer. She freely admits she has a faulty immune system!

She considers herself an expert at absorbing the hits, holding on to joy, and never losing sight of her goals.

Foreword

Accepting my disability started with a dream, a real clue that it was time to recognize some things. I had spent more than two years feeling like I was a cannonball in mid-flight, unwillingly launched and spinning end over end with no idea where I was going to land. Looking back on it now, the dream may have been God's way of telling me my tumbling was coming to an end.

Here's the dream:

I was leaving my brother and sister-in-law's place, but it wasn't really their house – you know how dreams do that. I was traveling a road I'd driven since I was 16 when suddenly I was in a field. I had no idea how I'd gotten there – had I made a turn? I tried to remember if I'd felt the bump of a curb (I hadn't) and looked back to see how far off the road I'd gone, but there was no road anymore. I realized I hadn't made a turn. The road was just gone.

I got out of the car and was standing on dirt with flowering weeds standing at least three-and-a-half feet tall all around, and I thought, "Well, the flowers are pretty." I was not thinking about finding my way back to the road, nor was I stressed about getting on with my trip. I knew this was where I was and wondered how it all happened.

I had this dream on June 11, 2011. Ten days later was the last day I tried to go to work – Multiple Sclerosis (MS) wouldn't let me. I couldn't walk and had wicked vertigo. I was thinking one thing and saying something else without knowing it, which is bad when you're being paid to be on the phone saying the same thing, with minor variations, up to 100 times a day. Most terrifying of all was how I was aware that I wasn't really thinking. I have a healthy IQ and am a college graduate, and I couldn't process questions, ideas, concepts – ANYTHING! I immediately stopped driving because I

7

couldn't trust that I would make the right choices behind the wheel.

Within a month, I had, with a lot of help, filed for Social Security Disability again, had a walker and a wheelchair delivered to my place, and had been told to move since I lived on the third floor and there was no way I could safely get out if there were a fire. Blood work showed that my B12 was in the gutter, so low that the health professional I saw at my Neurologist's office told me to take twice the recommended dose. Come to find out, low B12 is common in people with MS. AND, the type of MS I had was officially changed from the Relapsing-Remitting, where a patient loses a function for a brief period but it returns to normal, to Secondary Progressive, where the functions lost don't return to normal.

God has always been so present throughout my life in loud and quiet ways. But since that dream, His participation in my life has been enormous. I have experienced so much love and support from family and friends; I am so blessed and humbled. Truly the pretty flowers have made it easier to accept that there is no road for me anymore.

I have MS, but there are many afflictions – from bipolar disorder to diabetes to advancing age - that won't be ignored yet still leave us able to make decisions and have some control over our behaviors. I hope this book encourages you to identify your responsibilities and regain some of the empowerment your situation may have taken from you.

Definitions

I thought that, since I use many words in this book, it would be best to start off with the definitions of some of them as they apply to how they are used herein. I'm using a blend of the definitions found in Merriam-Webster and Oxford's, with my twist. None of my words have been redefined to placate anyone.

Empowered/Empowerment

Oxford: Empowerment: the process of becoming stronger and more confident, especially in controlling one's life and claiming one's rights

Websters: Empowered: having the knowledge, confidence, means, or ability to do things or make decisions for oneself.

I like both of these definitions! Discovering one's empowerment can be a process, as Oxford says, although I personally, after having a little taste of empowerment, started seeking more! And I appreciate the last four words of Webster's definition: making decisions for oneself. I would just add the word "healthy" or "quality" before the word decisions. I am perfectly capable of making "stubborn" or "stupid" decisions for myself – but we'll get into that later!

Accept/Acceptance

Oxford's first definition of accept is "consent to receive," like a present. HA! The synonyms they list include words like "welcome" and "acquire." Err, NO. Their second definition resonates better: believe or come to recognize as valid or correct. When reality has been forced upon you like my disability was on me, your goal has to be acceptance – acknowledging that things are irreparably different in every corner of your life. You are definitely going through the Kubler-Ross stages of grief – and acceptance is the hard-earned goal of the journey.

What do I mean when I say "accept" in this book? I mean to recognize and acknowledge (become reconciled to) that there is a new adjective describing me and you; to "take on" the new responsibilities that come with it, including identifying and tolerating its limitations so that we can re-invent who we are within our new boundaries.

Responsibility

The first definition in Oxford is the one I mean in this book: the state or fact of having a duty to deal with something. The synonyms listed there include words like authority (becoming an authority on the cause of your situation), management, and duty. I also liked "the state or fact of being accountable for something." And they threw in one greater one under the definition of responsible: morally accountable for one's behavior.

I also appreciated what Webster has to say on responsibility: the quality or state of being responsible; moral, legal, or mental accountability; reliability, trustworthiness; and something for which one is responsible, like a burden.

Grace

There are many definitions of this word, depending on the source of it.

First and foremost, God's Grace is defined as unmerited favor. It isn't earned, and if you've been the recipient of such, you know how unspeakably relieving and humbling it is. You will read of many episodes of God's grace shared with me in the coming chapters, but there's more.

Then there's the grace between people: the disposition to or an act or instance of kindness, courtesy, or clemency. I can't guess the number of times people – family, friends, strangers, have given me grace in these past ten years, but I can say that the effect of these actions has been the same as above: I was relieved and humbled every time.

The last one is the one I think all people could set the goal to adopt: the quality or state of being considerate or thoughtful. If I don't think I can exude this type of grace because of what my disease is doing to my body, I don't leave my apartment. This is a responsibility I hold as a Child of God, especially when faced with people who tell me how well their friend with MS is doing or launch into what they think I should be doing to improve my disease state.

1. What Now?

By the time I had "the dream," MS had been with me for over thirty years, though I'd only been diagnosed for nine. Still, I was only 50 years old, and though I was barely functioning from day to day, I knew that MS wouldn't kill me; it might shorten my life by about 10 years. Well, one of my grandmothers lived to be 97 years old, so I was still considering being on this planet for at least another thirty years! What was I going to do to fill my days?

It seemed that, once again, I was faced with the question that had challenged me for years – why am I here, and what should I be doing? I remembered two Bible verses that gave me my first solid ground to stand on:

Everyone who is called by my name, whom I created *for my glory*, whom I formed and made. – Isaiah 43:7

May the words of my mouth and the mediation of my heart be *pleasing in your sight* O Lord, my Rock, and my Redeemer. Psalm 19:14

I am here to glorify and please God.

As easy as that sounds, life can make glorifying and pleasing God hard to do. You might be familiar with the saying, **"God never gives you more than you can handle."** *How infuriatingly banal.* For years I responded to that phrase by saying, "Well, I wish He didn't think so highly of me!" In addition to being disabled by MS, I am divorced, have an estranged son and grandchildren I've never met, and have survived ovarian cancer. Though as I write this, I've only been officially "disabled" for a few years, MS has *always* limited my career, never having the energy it would have taken to do the jobs I so desired and for which I would have otherwise been well-suited. The world says I have earned a double serving of anger and bitterness.

I am not about to say I have never felt angry and bitter counting all the losses in my life because that would be a DAL (Daddy of All Lies.) We all know people who live their lives being unpleasant, bitter, spiteful, and such. It seems to be more common today than ever, something about only 'being human.'

Well, I'm human, but I am also Christian. I know that I'm not perfect. In fact, I'm a sinner, and I know that Jesus died for my sins, and I have asked Him in my heart to help me be **more** than just another animal occupying this planet for a while. I rest in the knowledge that I am a soul currently inhabiting a body and that when this vessel stops working, I get to go home for eternity. It seems logical that poor attitudes don't align with my goal to glorify and please God.

Again, please don't think I just brushed off any feelings of grief over saying goodbye to the future I had wanted, or the frustrations of dealing with government agencies, or the fury of being forced to accept that this body was never going to work like it was designed to perform. At one point, I referred to my reality as a Barrel Cactus – too big to get my hands around and guaranteed to hurt during the attempt.

Seriously, aside from my own personal goal, there was really no incentive to grasp my reality. I hated it. It was a real season of grief, confusion, and astonishment. I would sit on my couch watching TV, just waiting until it was late enough, say 8:00, to go to bed. I couldn't think! I was in such a fog. Then a car commercial would come on – the one with the red Cadillac CTS – and I'd find myself thinking, "I'm gonna get me one of those!" as you do with commercials. And then I'd remember that I couldn't drive anymore, never mind having the funds to make that kind of purchase or afford the insurance for it. It was what I call a "blindside" moment.

Another blindside hit happened every Saturday morning when I woke up. My habit had been to run down to the nearby grocery to pick up some fresh fruit and muffins for breakfast, especially if my son was home. So I'd wake and start planning to do that same thing, then I'd have to remind myself of how things now were, including that I no longer drove, and even if I did, I'd have to use my walker to get to the car, and I didn't have the strength or balance to put the walker in my car.

I also became aware of another habit: planning dishes I wanted to make and mentally adding items to my grocery list. For me, cooking was fun, and it was a way of showing love to those for whom I cooked. I had to remind myself that I didn't have the energy to cook anymore.

If you notice, in these "blindsided" examples, I'm not talking about no longer dreaming of home ownership or world travels. I was grieving over **everyday things**, tasks that really reached the core of who I am. MS took it all, even my ability to write by hand! So, I ask you, what should one aspire to when one can no longer "do?" What was I supposed to dream about now?

I am here to glorify and please God. These words provided some solace. I knew that, no matter what my body could no longer do, I could pray for others, and my writing ability - I had spent my career writing for businesses - would make it possible to share my faith. And, though I suddenly had very little face-to-face contact with people, I could let His Light shine through my eyes whenever I did see them. It felt good to identify something I *could* still do. That would be my goal. Not a new car, I didn't need a car, nor travel, the exhaustion and pain caused by my affliction had taken all the fun out of that, and not owning a home when I have no idea how long it will be before I am in an Assisted Living facility anyway. If you think it sounds bitter as you read this, it's because it is. Acceptance does not erase the pain of the loss; it just means that one has chosen to live in reality, no longer denying that it's not what one had wanted it to be.

A few caveats about acceptance:

It's a personal choice. There are a lot of people who will never live in acceptance, despite how much their loved ones wish they would. Others are unable, mentally or emotionally, to reach for it.

It doesn't happen overnight, and it's never complete. I had to decide I wanted to live in acceptance and commit to working the grieving process to achieve it. And that process (Denial, Anger, Bargaining, Depression and finally, Acceptance) takes time; a long, hard, angry, tearful time.

Where am I on acceptance? In some areas, I'm pretty good. In others, I'm a long way from it. And for me, it's a process that will start anew with each functionality loss.

Remember that infuriating quip about what God gives you? First, it isn't biblical. The Bible never mentions anything about it. But ignoring that, I decided that perhaps I have had so many burdens because He knows I will always run to Him *first*, and I never try to handle anything on my own. He freely gives unconditional acceptance to those who've asked His Son into their hearts.

FOR YOUR CONSIDERATION:

> Have you faced a sudden, drastic, life-changing, permanent loss that has rocked you to your core? Or perhaps it came on so slowly that you didn't recognize it until it was fully upon you.

> Are you denying your condition because you don't want this loss to be a part of your story?

> Or maybe, like me, you couldn't fight anymore, but you feel lost and angry.

> How are you doing at shedding the world's definition of success?

> Like I did, are you looking to redefine that word to identify goals you can achieve?

> Perhaps you're ready to throw this book across the room. That's OK, too.

Wherever you are on this new journey, you can make your future better by accepting the *responsibility to recognize* your situation. then identifying who you want to be in your new normal.

2. Who I Want to Be

¹⁷Though the fig tree does not bud
and there are no grapes on the vines,
though the olive crop fails
and the fields produce no food,
though there are no sheep in the pen
and no cattle in the stalls,
¹⁸ yet I will rejoice in the LORD,
I will be joyful in God, my Savior.

¹⁹ The Sovereign LORD is my strength;
he makes my feet like the feet of a deer,
He enables me to tread on the heights.

Habakkuk 3:17-19 New International Version (NIV)

I still had so much to figure out after adding "disabled" to the list of adjectives used to describe me. It was a profound time of "now what?" for me. The shock of this change was obvious and complete. I liken it to the feeling one may have upon receiving the phone call that a loved one has unexpectedly died. Of course, in this instance, my former self was deceased. Everything around me was the same but so different.

Along with the shock, however, came relief. I had finally admitted what I had to deny for so long; I could not work anymore. I didn't have to deny my reality or put that pressure on myself anymore. It felt odd but good. It took months, but I also learned to acknowledge my constant physical pain. I had been in pain for years but ignored it, too. I had spent much of my life denying my reality and didn't have to do that anymore. Still, my losses from my new reality were numerous and profound.

I loved working as part of a team to meet goals in a work

environment, being asked to be part of different projects for my perspective and abilities, and feeling valued, accepted and appreciated in a corporate setting. I enjoyed having a regular income, one with a little "scrounge" so I could treat myself to some extras now and again. I took for granted my ability to hop in my car on a whim and go somewhere. It was all gone so fast and so completely.

My new definition of a good day was any day I had the strength to take a shower **and** brush my teeth, both of which I now did while sitting.

I also now struggled with a degree of embarrassment, too. I was embarrassed when I had to go on food stamps – but I suddenly had no income. I was embarrassed to have to use a wheelchair whenever I did leave the house and that somebody had to push it. One of my first ventures out was to the DMV, where I surrendered my driver's license. I sat at least a foot below the counter. Most of the time, I left my apartment with my mother's help. It wasn't lost on me that though I was younger and looked able, my wheelchair was being pushed by a 77-year-old!

Fear was one of my constant companions in those first months of my new life. My decline had so blindsided me that I worried if I would keep declining at that same pace and which part of me would stop working next. I still wonder how much functionality I will actually lose over the years. My biggest fears are being unable to turn over in bed (something I experience whenever I have a fever) and being unable to scratch my own nose. I have been relieved to see that my decline has been quite slow, and I have even seen many improvements since June 2011.

I had identified what I most wanted to do – to bring God glory and make a positive difference, but how was a now disabled Susan going to do that when it took all I had to put clothes on and move to the Living Room? Doing a quick self-assessment, I admitted that my legs didn't work right anymore – the left one was worse than the right. It was also obvious then that my cognition was in the toilet, partly from the shock of this all happening so quickly but mainly from the disease. All my plans and dreams were dust, and that fresh wound still really hurt.

I mentioned before that in the year leading up to the "crash," as I call it, I had described myself as a cannonball in mid-flight, with no control of where I was going to land. Well, I finally hit the ground and, like any propelled object, was actually a few inches below the surface! Moreover, I hated where and how I was now more than when I was aimlessly tumbling through the sky! This was all so wrong – but I could admit that, on some level, it was correct – at least I didn't have to pretend anymore.

When I had the energy to consider my new situation, I was heartbroken and angry and frustrated that my potential, all the abilities God gave me, including creativity, intelligence, my ability to convey ideas to people and make things happen in the corporate world had been subjugated to my physicality. Yes, I had constant physical pain, but the emotional pain was so much more profound. IT WASN'T FAIR! I wasn't ready to be done interacting with coworkers, going to lunch, or making Saturday plans. I had no retirement money set aside. I had never had a passport. The list was endless.

This was also supposed to be the time for me to find a new man. My kids were grown, and I had healed enough from my previous marriage, so if God had a man for me, I was hoping we would meet. However, the idea of putting "Chick in a Wheelchair" on a dating site was ridiculous. Too, my problems were enough on their own. Adding a new person into the mix seemed foolish. I am pretty sure that I am meant to travel this life single.

An incredibly frustrating thing about Multiple Sclerosis is that no one can say for sure what the future holds for a person with the disease – it's different for each person. So beyond saying that my disease was progressing, there was no way to know if my legs would fail completely or stabilize where they were. B-12 improved my cognition, thankfully, but it was anyone's guess if it would stay that way or go down again. My arms were okay, but would they weaken, and if so, when? The bottom line for me was, "When am I going into

Assisted Living?" Well, nine years into it, I have help with cleaning, laundry, and occasional food preparation, and I do live in a handicap-accessible apartment, but Assisted Living still seems to be a few years off.

God had shown up in such mighty ways during those first months of my new life. I really wanted to share it all with people. One day, my sister-in-law said:

"Well, you've always wanted to write for Christ but were too busy writing for companies. Now you'll have time. You can start a blog!"

I hadn't even thought of that! I would start a blog highlighting all the God Things I had witnessed! I would do it as soon as I could. Six months before I launched it, but "Seeing Things Differently," and later Buhdiz, That's Why I became a reality and received wonderful feedback. I even gained a reader in California! I remember joyfully thinking, "I can still make a difference!" I could also still set and attain goals.

God showed me something else in the first eighteen months of my disability, which was quite unexpected! I was spending my days sitting in my Living Room watching my TV. I loved my apartment; it had three sliding glass doors on the North and East walls. The largest of these doors was in the Living Room, and I could see neighbors going about their lives not fifteen feet from my door. One day in a very hot July, I saw the same three people, a 20-something girl and guy, and a just-old-enough-to-walk baby boy, passing by my door, back and forth many times. I knew they weren't neighbors, so I wondered what they were doing here. The girl was constantly on the phone, and at one point, I heard her use the pronoun "her," and then the police arrived, and the girl broke down speaking with them.

OK, that tugged my heart. The girl had on ill-fitting leggings and a top that didn't cover her belly, and I started thinking that maybe she had recently given birth. I couldn't just leave her out there alone, crying! So I took my walker out to her and introduced myself, put my arm over her shoulders, and told her she didn't have to cry alone standing in the driveway of an apartment complex. She told me they had come to see her aunt, with whom they had briefly lived, but they couldn't raise her. The police had gone in to see if the woman was home. The guy and their child came back around the corner, saying it was too hot to sit in the car. I offered them a seat on my porch and brought ice water out for them. Eventually, the young man and his son came in to take advantage of the air conditioner. Sure enough, the girl's aunt had passed away. After a little while and some conversation, the trio left, and the coroner came. I was glad the girl didn't have to see that. I was extra exhausted with the walking, the heat, the emotional strain, and the energy to be a kind hostess. More importantly, though, was my happiness that I could be someone's "Jesus with Skin" right where I was!

God had shown me I could make Him smile through my blog and that He could use me right where I was. I could still be who I most wanted to be in spite of my disability. I thanked and praised Him loudly, but it didn't address all my concerns, especially all the things I was going to miss doing.

FOR YOUR CONSIDERATION

Where do you feel you are along this path: Still in mid-flight, with no idea where you'll land; or do you see that you've landed, and are trying to dig out from how far underground you are?

Have you considered your emotional pain yet? The sorrow you feel over the things that can never be again, the dreams that have died as a result of your life change. Think about it. Write it down. Scribble madly with a big red crayon. For yourself, because you and your feelings matter.

I encourage you to watch for opportunities to be Jesus with skin! It may be physically taxing, but you'll gain from it.

3. Accepting My Reality

I am Responsible for Accepting my Reality and Living Within It Imagine that all of your dreams are brutally taken away by something beyond your control. How are you to spend the rest of your life with dead dreams? I was lamenting about all the things I could no longer do when one of my physical therapists gave me a piece of advice I use to this day. He told me to identify what I love doing and figure out a way to keep doing it.

He told me about a patient who had always loved gardening and how, through raised beds, she continued working her garden, allowing her a way to keep "being herself." Writing and being creative is really who I am, so I will always write. I can no longer write by hand but still type on a computer. And when my hands no longer receive signals from my brain, I will purchase a product that will turn my voice into the printed word. I won't let physical limitations take writing from me. I have also noticed cognitive damage, so it takes longer for me to convey ideas properly, but I have a group of honest friends that review pieces like blog posts and letters before I release them! For this book, of course, I have a wonderful editor.

There are things that I truly can no longer do. One thing I have not been able to continue doing is entertaining in my home. My high school self dreamed of marrying well and throwing parties! I have thrown some really great parties – I love all the preparation and planning, making everything "just so." It was part of my love language, really, a way to show my appreciation for the people in my life. Somehow, buying a big sub sandwich and using paper plates just didn't feel the same as the old way. I have had one beautiful family brunch since this all started, though! I spent the entire week doing a little every day to make it happen – to meet my standards. I was very satisfied after it, so the exhaustion and days of nothing that followed it were easier to take. But don't get me started on what I can no longer do for Christmas!

I don't think I can accurately describe the depth of losses in my life. My pain is great, and though I already knew what pain causes, I discovered that I needed to accept the degree of ANGER I had because of all the pain.

FOR YOUR CONSIDERATION:

Whom do you want to be in your new reality? Remember, who you "are" is greater than what you "do."

What emotions are you dealing with regarding your new normal? Can you identify any that you fear or would prefer to ignore?

Are there "unknowns" that cause legitimate fear regarding your physicality? How can you prepare yourself for them, or what can you do to prevent their onset?

Have you permitted yourself to have a good cry over your losses?

Have you written down any of your frustrations regarding your new normal and listed activities you miss? It's a good way to know yourself, and something about seeing these things on paper is very validating, even if no one but you sees them.

What do you love doing? Have you thought about how you might still do it with modifications? You're worth doing that for yourself.

4. Limit My Negative Impact!

I am Responsible for Limiting My Negative Impact on Others

I was very blessed to be completely loved and cherished by my father, but like each of us, he had baggage and imperfections. When Dad was diagnosed with Type 2 Diabetes in his 30s, he was personally offended that his body wasn't "perfect," and though he was willing to go to the classes and such, he ultimately determined to continue to live his way, with the most minor changes to his diet and lifestyle. He always depended on my mom to tell him if his portion sizes were right.

Now, my dad was stubborn. I grew up with the understanding that stubbornness was good – it was how you got things done to your liking! Stubbornly ignoring a disease and the effect it had on one's eyesight, though, was not wise. I remember riding with him as we went down the expressway while I told him he was crossing the centerline, at which point I thought, "I can't be proud of Dad's behavior right now." His denial of reality was literally threatening the lives of other people. His "stubbornness" has crossed the line. His actions were stupid! This is a moment I'll never forget.

I lived my life to that point, wanting to behave in a way that made not just me but my maternal grandmother proud. That one incident with my dad had me adding my children to the list of people I want to be proud of my actions. I don't want them shrugging with resignation, saying, "That's the way she was," regarding my stupid actions at my death.

I have long said "Stubborn" and "Stupid" have a very close relationship. As a word person, the first thing I notice is that the two words begin with the same three letters. As I pondered their relationship further, I could envision a line on which a person's actions were measured as positive or negative, with degrees of how good or bad the actions were. "Stubborn" was immediately followed by "Stupid," and the delineation between them would be so faint it would be very hard to see by the person walking the line.

ACTION LINE

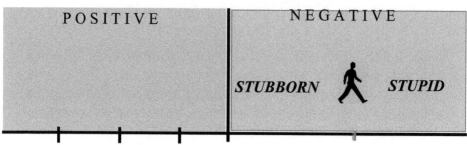

As a person living with a "new normal," I truly didn't know what I could or couldn't do around the house. Most days, I didn't try to do anything – I remember both showering AND brushing my teeth made it a "good" day those first months.

In my defense, living in the "Stubborn" zone had been my way of life for probably 20 years, starting even before the end of my marriage. I was undiagnosed, so I held myself to high standards as to what I should accomplish day-to-day. Later, as a single mother, I had boys who needed emotional rebuilding along with food, clothing, and a place to live. I had a college degree, experience, and skills that were needed in the work world. It didn't matter how exhausted I was, I had responsibilities to meet. Especially before my diagnosis, I thought all single mothers felt as exhausted as I was, so I did what I had to do and moved on. And I continued ignoring my body even after the diagnosis, seeing no other choice (I had applied for disability and been declined, and an attorney told me I was too young.) As a result, my "how to be disabled" education began with learning to listen to my body! I came to realize that I was almost always in pain, particularly in my legs and upper back. This was muscular pain – something specific to neurological conditions. I had just never *ACKNOWLEDGED IT!*

As I improved over the months and had more days when I felt

"able," I was excited to see what I could do again! Mind you, this was all brand new to me. I still only had the logical head knowledge that I was never going to be as functional as I had been. It is like a toddler being told that the stove is hot. My son could point to the oven and say "hot," but he didn't *know* "hot" until he had a personal experience with it. I needed concrete proof, I needed to know my limits, to really know my "hot." Experimenting was how I learned. It's also how I became aware of that whole stubborn-stupid thing.

The first thing I wanted to do on my good days was cook! My son had moved home to care for me, and he was working full-time, too. I wanted to do what I could to "pull my own weight," so to speak. As food preparation is one of the ways I show love, I wanted to at least have dinner made for him whenever he got home. However, long before the task was accomplished, I found that I was completely wiped out and my arms too weak to stir, lift or carry! Instead of my son coming home and relaxing before dinner, he had to come in and complete the dinner I had started. I eventually accepted that cooking the way I had before was no longer an option, and he made dinner for us after relaxing for a while. When he suggested that way of doing things, I understood that it was more respectful to him to do it that way – his timing, his meal preparation. I also stopped making the grocery list.

So, maybe I could do laundry! Yes, the laundry room was at the other end of my very long apartment building. But I figured I could put the laundry basket on my walker, make my way down there, and stay through there for the 90 minutes it took for the whole process. I soon learned just sorting the items before I left my apartment exhausted me. But never to be deterred, I decided I'd sort one day and trek down to the washers & dryers the next. Tried it – I had to lie down afterward without folding the fresh clothes, much less putting them away. Laundry came off my list, too.

Then there was the day that the trash in my kitchen smelled. My son was at work, and I decided I had enough energy to take the trash out to the dumpster – it wasn't that far from my door. I loaded the trash bag onto my walker - I was realistic enough to know I had to use it. I may have mentioned before that God gave me 60 inches in height. The opening of the dumpster was over my head – which had never been a problem before. Well, now I didn't have the strength to lift the bag to get it into the dumpster! Fortunately, a neighbor from another building came along and hoisted it over for me. That was a little embarrassing, but it also made for a good laugh.

Like a horse in a new pasture, I "ran the fences" to establish my limits. I was sad and frustrated to see that the most basic activities were more than I could do. Oh, and whenever I would engage in cooking or whatever, I would be non-functional the next day or two to the point of being unable to think, in addition to physical exhaustion and pain. These "pay-days" gave me the opportunity to identify "stupid" behaviors: anything I couldn't finish myself or cost me great recovery time. Okay, I thought, good to know. I viewed the pay-days as a punishment by the MS for trying to ignore my new reality and decided they alone were worth not overdoing it. Yet I was still fuzzy on what I could do without repercussions – and that's why the line between Stubborn and Stupid is so hard to see! Time and again, I found myself in the middle of Stupid territory before I knew it. I had to really think over every step I'd taken to see the point where I needed to stop to avoid inconveniencing another person or costing myself. It was another entirely new process for me, and I hate being a novice. I made myself recognize every positive action I took, even if I did too much, reminding myself that I would eventually see that thin gray line before I crossed it, no matter what activity I was doing. I purposely set it a series of mini-goals: to more quickly identify that I was once again in Stupid territory; to become aware of my own condition as I crossed that thin gray line – to know how the line looked and felt; to notice I had crossed that line; and finally, to monitor me to stop my activity before I crossed into Stupid!

As with all learning processes, it took a long time, with lots of errors and missteps along the way, but because I knew God accepted me just as I was, I eventually accepted myself throughout this learning process, something that I could never have done earlier in my life – I'm goal oriented, remember.

Stupid actions usually cause two things:

They cause more stress and ability than a person has available to use, and They negatively impact at least one other person.

When we consider the example of my father, he didn't have the ability to see well, and though he would deny it if he were here today, that did cause his body stress. It certainly caused ME stress as his passenger, and it eventually caused an accident in a car he was driving for someone else, costing them money!

My own stupid actions cost me the energy I don't have, and when I push myself, my old "perfectionist" tendencies usually resurface, adding emotional stress to my physical stress. Then I pay for it with a number of "nonfunctioning days" when I can't think and am in physical pain. As for the negative impact on others because of my stupid actions, I've already mentioned my son, but here's a beautiful experience I was given that made it crystal clear:

My nephew informed his parents of his engagement to his girlfriend! They were living in New York City, and the wedding would take place in her hometown in Connecticut.

One of my brother Russ' first thoughts was, "Susi is going to need to get there a day early to rest before the wedding." While he and his crew drove to the location a few days before the big event, Russ purchased plane tickets for my mother, my son, and myself. We traveled on Wednesday so that I could indeed have time to rest from the travel day. My son was included as our helper and driver – our destination was about three hours from the airport. I felt so loved and accepted that Russ would make those arrangements for me! And while I was resting over the next few days and Mom was busy doing pre-wedding things, Russ made sure to check to see if I needed anything, bringing lunch back to me when they had been out and about! During the entire five-day trip, my family – to the last person – showed they had thought of ways to make things easier for me. The night before the wedding, we all gathered at this restaurant/bar to spend time and celebrate. I needed to visit the facilities and mapped out the way to get my wheelchair through the tables and chairs to get there. I was touched to see my brother's family neighbor right behind me as I got to the restroom. She managed the door for me and stayed until I was finished, just there in case I needed any help (as a Physician's Assistant, she was concerned that I might fall.) There was so much love and care shown to me during that trip! It was humbling, and it helped me see that what I did impacted people. So many extra steps had been put in place in recognition of my limitations, things people just did because they cared!

Part of the result of me staying at the party the night before was my very limited energy the day of the wedding. I had to leave the reception about halfway through it, but when he learned that I was leaving, my sweet nephew (the groom) collected some of the terrific desserts for me to take with me! That whole fantastic experience helped me understand that I had some responsibilities associated with my new normal and one of them was to do what I could to limit the negative impact I had on others above what they already happily did for me!

The awareness that I had a *responsibility* gave me a new sense of empowerment, something that had been lost when I became disabled. God quickly showed me many areas where I could exert some control to lessen the negative impacts on others, and when I say quickly, I mean He downloaded them, in outline form, into my brain in seconds. I give Him all the credit because I don't think that way, or that fast, or that completely, ever. This book is the result.

How can I make things easier for other people?

When considering my new empowerment, something struck me anew: my weight. It is entirely possible that in the future, I will need assistance transferring from a wheelchair into a bed and visa-versa. Someone else may have to make that happen for me. I have always been a stress eater, so throughout my marriage and divorce, I got quite overweight. I joined Weight Watchers when I weighed 194 pounds, losing 50 pounds in less than a year! I fell off the Weight Watchers wagon before reaching my goal weight because of stress from the MS diagnosis and my then job, but I regained less than ten pounds between 2003 and 2011. With disability and the accompanying depression, however, potato chips and chocolate became my friends, and I ballooned back to 177 pounds. My "ideal" weight is 125 pounds.

My new goal enabled me to grasp that it would be best if a future Aide didn't have to move more of me than there should be. But how to accomplish weight loss when I am over 50 and unable to exercise? Eventually, I saw something on Facebook called "The 30-Day Challenge" and decided to try it. I lost 17 pounds in the first three weeks! Shortly thereafter, I decided to go Paleo, which is grass-fed beef and organic chicken or pork and wild-caught fish, plus cruciferous vegetables. Nothing white, nothing processed, NO sugar. Aside from the weight loss, I felt markedly better day-to-day, making it easier to do the cooking needed to follow the diet! I still have days when I know I shouldn't try to handle knives or hot pans, so I permit myself to have the occasional pizza or sub, but I don't let myself get too far off track. As I write this, I am 20 pounds from my goal!

In the light of empowerment, I also considered my family. It seemed at one point as though they had all gotten together to discuss my situation and had come to the conclusion that I should move into an assisted living facility – where meals and daily assistance were provided – and my living space was cut down to one room with a twin bed! I panicked upon hearing this – I was both afraid and angry at the idea! I came to the conclusion that their thinking was also fear-based: that they would worry less if I was "taken care of" as my brother and his wife were still working full time, and my mom was aging. This is when I asked my neurologist what she thought about the idea, and she totally dismissed it, saying that in no way was I near needing that kind of help. My family stood down from their stance. But the lesson for me was there.

It is my responsibility to map out the future with my loved ones using very concrete, tangible markers to identify when additional help is necessary. I want to be the key decision-maker in my future as much as I can be! That means I look at my situation as clinically as possible, observing challenges and losses without defenses. It's my job to always be aware of myself. In the situation in the previous paragraph, it was February, and I have Seasonal Affective Disorder – so my depression is at its worst from January through April. My family was not as aware of that as I was. It's also my job to report any falls I have to my doctor. Fortunately, that doesn't happen much anymore, what with my power wheelchair and all. I don't have a spouse who might assist in these things, so I can't pawn stuff off to him as my dad did to my mom regarding his diet. But I surely won't be excluded from deciding what's best for me!

In my situation, cognitive abilities are also lost. I am aware of my own cognitive losses, and those bother me more than my visible physical ones. I have asked my brother if he will take over my budget in the event I am unable to keep it. I may have mentioned that math is my second language, and I'm not that fluent in it! Excel helps me tremendously, but if the time comes, I've made arrangements.

As for now, I live independently, preparing my own food for the most part. I have help once a week, a person that cleans and does laundry, plus helps with things I cannot do – like getting things out from under my bed.

Another conscious move I can make to minimize my negative impact on others is to always be aware of my day-to-day limitations. There are many days when pain or fatigue leaves me rather unpleasant, no matter what. It's a very easy thing to just stay in on days like those. As I want to sign God's light wherever I go, I know on bad days, it won't shine through. This world has enough negative energy already – I will not willingly add to it.

The same goes for planning activities. When I remember working every day, taking meetings, planning events, meeting deadlines…that was so fun! Now, if I have a one-hour dental appointment on Monday, I know not to plan to do anything on Tuesday. It's the same for anything I want to do. My Sister-in-Love recently took my mom and me to the beach. It was a wonderful afternoon – great weather, beautiful sights, and time together – I will always treasure that memory! I was busy for about seven hours total that day. And I was flat as a pancake for the next five – but it was so worth it! I knew ahead of time not to expect much from myself after the trip – so I wasn't shocked or angry when it played out. That does mean I don't do as much as I'd like to or as I once did. But this is now, and I have a realistic grip on the way it needs to be. I don't inconvenience others by agreeing to do more than I can. I don't fail to meet expectations, either. I carefully choose how to spend my energy, and God always gets the first of it. Funny thing – I can do so much more when I am following His lead!

Before you start thinking I have it all neatly wrapped up with a bow, please know that mine is a progressive disease, and I will face new losses as time advances. I will be constantly re-evaluating what I can no longer do. Knowing me, I won't glibly accept each new loss, either. There will be new grief, starting with denial, then a good solid dose of anger. Achieving acceptance is a long process, and it's new every time.

That doesn't give me a pass to keep doing what I no longer can, however. When I overdo it, someone else always pays. If I truly desire to minimize the negative effect I have on others, I must accept, with grace, each new loss. Apologies mean nothing if I keep apologizing for the same wrong behavior!

Have you had the experience of going somewhere with your new baby? Once she's dressed and fed, you need to load her, her bag, a stroller, and maybe her car seat into the vehicle. I have often likened myself to a baby when going somewhere in my manual wheelchair. My friend has to push me out of my apartment, hold my stuff while I get in, then fold my chair and put it in the back of the car, and do it in reverse when we get to our destination! It's a lot to ask of someone. It's an inconvenience, and there's no way around it if I'm to go with my friend.

I am an inconvenience. Well, that hurts, another in a long line of verbs I never wanted to be associated with myself. Now if any of my friends were to read this, they'd instantly deny it because they are sweet, loving people. But it is what it is. No, I never resented all the extra steps it took to load my child into a car, but it was EXTRA, taking time and energy. This is another reason I won't permit myself to be bitter or angry, or otherwise downtrodden about my life. How many times would YOU do all that "EXTRA" if the person for whom you were doing it was a bummer to be with? No, I have decided that I will always be thankful and positive for all the extra things people do in consideration of me. It goes back to understanding that nobody owes me anything – what they do is out of the goodness in their hearts. The least I can do is try to bless them while we're together!

FOR YOUR CONSIDERATION:

Can you call to mind anyone in your life that has been living over the line into "Stupid" territory? How did their behaviors make you feel?

Have you found yourself defending your actions to others? Sneaky reality check: If you say "Yes, but…" the Yes is the only part that matters.

Can you think of a time when someone else "picked up the slack" for your inability to do something? Same reality checks here, too.

Are you prepared to take the responsibility for your new normal, in order to feel more empowered to handle it?

How do you feel about the word inconvenience? Can you think of ways people just do things for you? How have you responded to these kindnesses? How will you respond in the future?

5. Admit and PROCESS Anger!

I have to Acknowledge and Deal with My ANGER!

Somewhere during my development, I determined that 1. Pretty is good, and ugly is bad; and 2. Happy is pretty, and angry is ugly.

I'm not suggesting that anyone in my upbringing purposely taught me these things, but it's what I learned. As a right, proper Texas girl whose only interest in football was the pretty, high-kicking girls on the sidelines, I always wanted to be pretty, and remember: Pretty=good. At this age, I had long blond hair and was cute as a button, so looking back, I see I had pretty in the bag.

Now, another screwy idea that formed firmly in my brain was that whatever caused me the pain was my fault. It might have something to do with merrily engaging in some activity and then getting in trouble for it, but whatever the cause, I have always thought, deep down, that any pain I experienced could be avoided in the future by changing my behavior. I gleefully entered adulthood unconsciously, thinking that whenever I encountered something that caused me pain, I had to identify what I'd done to cause it, then NEVER DO AGAIN! Do you sense the underlying theme here? I honestly didn't until much later than this.

And just to provide way too much insight into the workings of my mind, pain caused my face to look ugly, and ugly was bad, so the pain was completely linked to bad and ugly. To this day, I still think that's not all wrong. Anyway, let's pull out of the workings of my young brain and move to more current times.

My thirties were a decade of tremendous pain. Multiple Sclerosis was first theorized as the cause of my physical problems,

33

though not verified; we lost the house I thought would be our home, my emotionally-abusive marriage died, and I had ovarian cancer the same year that my eldest child moved in with his father and severed ties with me. I did my best to devote myself to healing my youngest child while working full time, attempting to recover from the incredible losses I had suffered, and ignoring the realities of my undiagnosed disease.

True to form, I determined my first step in recovering was to identify what I had done to cause myself all this pain. This is where you take a bird's eye view of things and logically pinpoint your missteps. I could identify the mistakes that led to my divorce and how to avoid repeating them, i.e., waiting for God to bring the right man to my door. I would spend years trying to identify what I had done to earn my eldest's wrath and eventually accepted that the problem had little to do with me. I had ideas on how I had gotten the cancer, but it was gone, and I was clear from that. And the MS? It had just been an idea anyway – I didn't have the time or energy to give it much thought.

My forties brought the verification of MS, which provided me with vindication and relief – yes, there was something wrong with me, and it had nothing to do with me being spoiled and lazy, as my husband had suggested when we were still married. I also learned there was no known cause of the disease: nothing I had done brought it on. This was my first real encounter with pain without my input. There was nothing I should have done differently, nor anything I could do now to change the fact that I had MS and had had it since I was at least seventeen years old. It would have happened no matter what I did. Kind of an odd thought.

The diagnosis did nothing to change my everyday life, however. I still worked full-time and focused on my role as a mom. Eventually, I became a speaker associated with the drug company that created the disease-modifying drug I took to keep MS at bay, and really enjoyed the travel and experiences I had interacting with and encouraging other people with MS around the country. I even developed a few comedy routines related to the disease, and they met with great success! I was experiencing success on multiple levels: my work was valued and satisfying, my life experience and personality were appreciated, I had taken positive steps to help my remaining child heal and grow into a fine adult, and I was healing from the losses of my thirties. Life overall was pretty good. With my youngest in high school, I started envisioning my life after he was off to college, the dreams I would chase when my primary role as Mom was over. My future seemed so bright! Sure, I had made changes to accommodate the MS – but I could do anything!

The economic downturn in 2008 brought an end to my very lucrative work as a writer for various companies, and the stress of my father's death in early 2009 opened the door for the MS to do all it could to destroy me. I did get full-time work in a call center just as my savings was all used up in 2010, a job I dragged myself to until I literally could no longer pretend to function.

Now, I'm going to throw some Psychology 101 at you.

Pain causes anger. It's why there is often an expletive uttered after a person hits his head on the car door frame. Further, any kind of loss causes pain. And again, pain causes anger. Well, my thirties were filled with losses and pains, and my forties carried losses and pain, too. And my way of dealing with anger put me on a hamster wheel, repeating the same actions and never getting anywhere new.

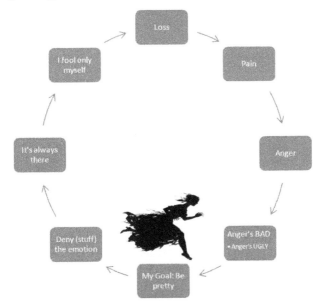

The sudden inability to work or drive at fifty years old, however, brought such overwhelming losses I literally couldn't process it all. I had lost any hope of creating income, of my ability to walk (WHAT?), or even to drive. Suddenly gone were any hopes of buying a new car, ever purchasing my own home, funding my own vacations, ANYTHING! Eventually, I slid into my old pattern of trying to identify where I'd screwed up so I could fix it, but there was nothing. I understood that I had MS, but I'd had it for years, and I could still function and pursue my dreams! Surely there was something I could change to get back to normal.

In an attempt to change how things now were, I would be very careful not to do much one day in the hopes of having more energy the next. Over and over, however, I would wake up that second day with no more ability than I had on the first. It made no sense. I even wondered if my dreams (I'm always walking and working in my dreams) somehow wore my body out. I knew I had gone too far with that thought, but there was no answer to my question "WHY" other than the fact that we live in a fallen world, and stuff happens to the just and the unjust alike. When I would verbalize my question, my sweet son (who had moved home to care for me) would always say, "Because you have MS." I had done nothing and could do nothing to change my condition. Wait, what?

If I hadn't done anything, there was nothing I could FIX to keep it from happening again. So on top of the other losses, I had also lost control over my own body! (Loss leads to pain...pain leads to anger...)

Now, I don't know about you, but I prefer having a modicum of control in my life. Control is good. Surprises can be bad.

That was the crux of my problem: I was angry over the loss of control. All of these losses had hit, and I was utterly powerless to change anything. This horrible thing had happened to me *just because*. I didn't cause it, I didn't earn it, and no one made it happen to me. It made no sense!

My anger was profound. But remember: anger is bad and ugly. I want to be good and pretty. So I tried to do as I'd always done –

stuff the anger and deny it. I didn't do that very well – no one ever does. My son noticed the bite in my comments about things on TV, even. Sinicism snuck through everything I said or thought. My counselor helped me see that I needed to identify the sources of my anger and deal with it. Remember, though, we're talking about 50+ years of anger! The task seemed daunting, but I could see that holding the anger in was blocking my goal of shining God's light in my part of the world. I needed to confront, process, and deal with my anger.

By this time, I thought of Anger as a huge, mucus-oozing tornado-shaped monster. I was afraid of it, afraid I would be consumed by it and lose myself – everything I had worked to develop to be "Me."

Some people choose to take their anger out on others - usually, people that were uninvolved in the real cause of that person's anger. The unjust criticism of the coffee shop employee, the snipe at a coworker, the angry response to a spouse, and the verbal or physical abuse to a child are all inappropriate, common examples of mishandled anger. The ugliness in this action is the worst. It turns the angry person into an abuser. Well, I would never be that kind of person!

Some learn to turn their anger against themselves – constantly playing berating tapes in their heads that say things like "You're so stupid!" "Why don't you ever measure up!" and similar nasty thoughts. That person defeats himself right out of the gate - it is unlikely he will ever achieve his dreams or make lasting relationships – except with those who think of him as he does and reinforce that his thoughts are correct. This turns the angry person into a person who exudes pathos – you don't really like him – but you're not really sure why.

I am mostly in this last category – the ones who "stuff" their anger and pretend it doesn't exist. I am a little bit of the previous person, too, if I'm honest. This method never works – the anger shows itself in nasty little ways – sarcasm, snide comments, and "jokes" that are more hurtful than funny. The flavor this person leaves is bitter, though she may be completely unaware of it.

I mentioned above that my son noticed the bitterness in what I thought were funny comments over things we saw on the television. I thank God that he called me out about them! Bitterness is a sign of some deep-seated anger in a person – a symptom of a larger problem. Sadly, bitterness is acceptable and reasonable in today's world.

It *is* perfectly natural to become bitter when faced with a society that can't really accommodate your limitations. If your energy is limited, you are not able to attend evening functions. You miss out on small groups, choir practice, going to the bar, and any other events that would provide fellowship because they take place when the *majority* of people can utilize them – at night. Being unique is good, but it hurts that my differences keep me so far out of the majority.

Another source of bitterness can be government and non-profit assistance agencies. While on the surface, there are programs available to assist the disabled, it seems they are designed to serve as few people as possible. It is understandable that measures are in place to avoid abuses, but that really means the disabled person is given a hard time when times are already hard. On average, a person can expect a three-year fight to gain access to *earned* Social Security Disability benefits.

The death of dreams is by far the bitterest pill. Dreams die hard for everyone, but for the disabled, the dreams that die can include the chance for marriage or love, a stimulating career, travel, living independently, or caring for others. Add to that the isolation that is a part of being physically limited, and the disabled person can have a lot of time to stew in bitter juices.

We have learned to shrug and think nothing of a bitter disabled person, maybe to feel bad for her. That "emotional stink" is a natural repellant, too. I know I have found ways to distance myself from a bitter person while feeling bad for him or her. Well, the last thing I wanted as a newly disabled person was someone well-earned, understanding pity and distancing! And remember, my overall goal continued being glorifying God and reflecting His love to everyone. As my emotional state was blocking my goal, I needed to deal with that beast.

Stored anger leads to bitterness. I had been "avoiding" or denying my anger all my life, to my own peril. The effects of "stuffed" anger are noticeable in behavior, but it also impacts physical health, causing hair loss, ulcers, and digestive issues. Ignored negative emotions can be linked to obesity. Anger can cause dental problems in addition to depression and anxiety. There were theories in the 1980s that it causes cancer, too.

Over time, my counselor showed me that anger was just an emotion, on the same level as happiness and sorrow. She pointed out that all our emotions are God-given so that we can fully experience everything here on earth. She also said that I have control over anger – that I could pull it out for a time, then put it away and go on with my day. Though it takes you seconds to read, this concept took a year or more for me to really grasp. Anita helped me turn that huge, ugly tornado into what it always was: Something designed for my benefit that I could learn to effectively use and dismiss. I spent months journaling about my anger: All the causes, whether my anger was just or due to my misunderstanding of a situation, my true feelings – and yes – there were lots of tears, then the blessed relief of releasing it all. By that, I mean some of it, upon reflection, disappeared like a fog in my hand, and the rest – the ones with no answer or resolution – I lifted to God to carry as I am too small to try to any longer.

So why do I face this struggle? Because anger won't be denied, and it takes an active role in destroying a person's life. While society no longer requires people to "stuff" or deny anger, it is still the learned behavior of people in dysfunctional homes, and it seems there will always be plenty of those.

Now, am I sitting here on a gray January day, suggesting that I no longer have problems with dealing with my past or processing new anger? Absolutely NOT! My goal here is to share my experiences and TRUTH with you – not to weave some happily ever after story! What I've learned is that anger itself isn't ugly, but I have a responsibility to make sure that what I do with it isn't, either.

FOR YOUR CONSIDERATION

Ask God to show you how anger has affected you.

How have you learned to deal with the anger in your life? Do you dump it on others? Drink until it's gone? Beat yourself up with it? Or are you one of the rare few who have always processed it and moved on?

As you're probably not in that last category (let's be real), what is one positive move you can make to start defeating the anger inside you?

Draw a picture of the anger you carry with you.

Ask God to help you begin the long process of identifying, validating, and releasing your anger so that you can more clearly shine His light.

6. Earn Respect

It's my Job to make it easy for others to respect my choices

Let's just make this clear: It's impossible to respect another person's bad choices. From drunk driving to irresponsible procreating, people around the world shake their heads in disgust. There is nothing to respect in those person's actions.

Another point of clarification: Even though I'm disabled, NO ONE OWES ME ANYTHING. If your disability is the result of another person's actions, once you have a settlement from that person, NO ONE OWES YOU ANYTHING! Not the government, not your spouse, your children, your extended family, your church - any help or assistance given from another person is a gift. Gifts are given out of love, or respect, or just the goodness of the giver. No one is ever owed a gift. However, there are many non-profit organizations whose goals are to help people with certain disabilities, and I encourage you to look into any that might specialize in your particular affliction.

It is so easy to fall into behavioral traps as we deal with life-changing disabilities – behaviors that leave onlookers calling a person pitiful or shameful. Here are a few examples.

The "Nothing is ever good enough" Whiner. This person's life took a bad turn somewhere along the way: a car accident that left her with physical problems; a change in his chemical makeup that made him allergic to everything; she got laid off from the job she'd had for many years and never got another one. Key to the Whiner's situation is that the incident that caused it, and the failure to move on from it wasn't their fault, it happened to them. This person has been cheated, and nothing is ever good enough to please him or her. They can be hyper-sensitive to perceived slights, seeing attempts at humor as personal insults. Any problem the Whiner has must be solved by others at their expense, but anything that is done for them is lacking in some way. Any solution offered is met with "but..." followed by why it won't work.

The Whiner has this misconception: that *everyone owes* her because of what happened. Nothing can be further from the truth. A person's happiness or satisfaction is his own responsibility. The Whiner has the responsibility to deal with what's happened and start taking some adult responsibility.

The "Eeyore." This kind of person seems to have accepted his sorry lot in life, but it is his only topic of conversation. Regardless of the subject currently being discussed, The Eeyore's contribution will be *his* problem-centric. We have all been witness to this: Someone joyfully comments on the beautiful weather, sparking others to happily join in. Eeyore will add "But the barometric pressure is making my bursitis really bad." Someone mentions the fiftieth anniversary of the Moon landing, and an Eeyore will respond "I wonder if the humidity is as bad on the Moon as it is here. I can hardly breathe with this humidity!" You get the idea.

To an extent, we can all be this last type, at least temporarily. It's the "Everything's perfect" Refuser. To be clear, this is NOT someone with Alzheimer's or Dementia, nor is it the person in the midst of coming to terms with a new reality. The Refuser will not own their reality and consciously participate in dealing with it. This is the person who won't take the medication to fight whatever ails them and viciously defends the reasons they have not to make themselves better. The Refuser can be one who denies a serious financial change, continuing to blindly spend despite it. My dad's refusal to stop driving falls under the Refuser category. Alcoholics and other addicts are always Refusers. Everyone else sees the reality of the Refuser's situation and wonders why the Refuser won't.

There are benefits to these behaviors, of course. A person dealing with a new disability has so much to process, that anger and frustration demand recognition by self and by others. Denial is also a reasonable response, although it ultimately hurts the person more than helps.

These three are just examples I have noticed and choose not to emulate; no doubt there are many others. Christ is the best way to help overcome these behaviors because His purposes are greater than the individual working to carry them out. Recognizing that my work as a Christian hadn't changed even though my life had provided motivation to keep going, though I wasn't as aware of biblical examples then as I am now. Check out Paul's attitude in Philippians 1:12-22 below. To set the scene, he was imprisoned in a Roman facility for preaching the good news. The fact that he was a Roman citizen (which traditionally would have prevented imprisonment) meant nothing because the Roman elite so feared the Gospel. At that time, prisoners were not fed or clothed – their friends and family members had to provide for them. They were chained to these high-powered guards 24/7. Look what he wrote to his friends!

[12] Now I want you to know, brothers and sisters, that what has happened to me has actually served to advance the gospel. [13] As a result, it has become clear throughout the whole palace guard and to everyone else that I am in chains for Christ. [14] And because of my chains, most of the brothers and sisters have become confident in the Lord and dare all the more to proclaim the gospel without fear...[20] I eagerly expect and hope that I will in no way be ashamed, but will have sufficient courage so that now as always Christ will be exalted in my body, whether by life or by death. [21] For to me, to live is Christ and to die is gain. [22] If I am to go on living in the body, this will mean fruitful labor for me.

"If I am to go on living in the body, this will mean fruitful labor for me." This verse hits me anew every time I read it. I've already established I'll be here for a while yet, in this diminished capacity. And if I'm here, I want my labors to be fruitful for Christ. If I get stuck in a behavior that is unpleasant to others, how can I accomplish that?

If respect is the goal, identify, change, or avoid behaviors that are hard for others to respect. For me, Christian counseling helped me pull out of whining and denial before I could spread their vile essence very far. But again, it didn't happen overnight!

FOR YOUR CONSIDERATION

Have you ever thought less of someone because of her behavior? What specifically did you think that person should have done differently?

Have you fallen into some of the behaviors listed above? Can you think of another type of behavior you want to avoid?

Why might spending a little time in on any negative behavior benefit you?

I wanted to change my attitude and behavior; Do you?

Have you ever considered counseling to help deal with your new reality? Are there concerns that have kept you from seeking that assistance?

7. Recognize My Needs, Get Assistance

I am Responsible for Requesting Assistance…which means

I need to Recognize that I NEED it

How does one know that her reality isn't the same as everyone else's? There can be a great chasm between knowing you have a disease and recognizing its day-to-day impact on your life. Though I hadn't been aware of it at the time, I was living under a veil of denial that kept me from seeing reality for at least 20 years before I saw the truth.

As I mentioned, I spent many years chiding myself for not doing as much as my friends did with ease. I would exhaust them so quickly, while they just kept going! I just could not figure out how they accomplished so much more than I did. Sure, there had been a diagnosis of Muscular Dystrophy when I was 17, but that had been overturned! Not getting an MS diagnosis when I was 31 had my then-husband determining that my lethargy was because I was spoiled and lazy. When I did finally get that diagnosis ten years later, everything fell into place, and I could accept that there was a legitimate "why."

Nine years after the diagnosis, my family members were moving me from my third-floor abode to a first-floor unit at the insistence of my Neurologist. During the process, someone noticed the layers of dust and cobwebs on things. That kind of housekeeping had fallen off my "To-Do" list years before. Shortly after the move, my brother and his wife offered to pay for cleaning services. It was a blessing to me for sure, but I didn't really connect the dots that were right in front of my face.

Until they offered that help, I assumed everybody who worked forty hours a week and was raising children skipped housework because it was too much trouble. After my move, I learned that my sister-in-law worked full time, managed their three children's activities, dusted and vacuumed weekly, changed the sheets on their beds routinely, and even moved furniture somewhat regularly to clean behind and under it! I had been unable to consider doing that for years.

A few years before disability forced its way into my life, I purchased a fancy electric toothbrush. It came programmed for a two-minute brushing cycle – and I was appalled. I mean, teeth are important, but they really expected folks to be able to stand for two whole minutes – how unrealistic is that?

My misunderstanding of the toothbrush standards, and my brother's offer for housekeeping assistance, combined with my then-new disabled status helped me accept that I *was* different, and needed to take responsibility for identifying ways that I might need assistance. I realized that others might have looked upon the condition of my home as pitiful or even shameful. "She let her house become so gross," some might say – and by some, I mean it's something I might have said once upon a time. I was of course amazed at this realization, and as a person focused on accepting reality, I became determined to avoid falling into what I considered other shameful behaviors.

I focused on developing the ability to identify my need for help, then requesting and accepting it, with grace. At the same time, I needed to discover the kinds of help that were available. I started with my doctor's office.

My Neurologist set me up with Physical and Occupational therapy, right in my home. The therapists came to me because I could no longer drive. Insurance companies approve a certain number of visits for these types of therapy, but the providers can obtain approval for more visits based on patient needs. I later learned that I could request more therapy as I noticed new disabilities, and have done so a few times over the years.

EMPOWERED THOUGH DISABLED

I am amazed by the depths of knowledge Physical and Occupational therapists just carry in their brains! Generally, Physical therapists specialize in how the body moves, while Occupational therapists are focused on treating things that keep patients from doing daily tasks. These can range from simple tasks to complex job activities.

These therapists came for the first time in the early days of my disability. I may have mentioned how appalled I was seeing them come in with a walker (I'm not 80!) and a manual wheelchair. These items had been ordered specifically for me based on my height and weight. For a long time, Physical therapists worked with me to strengthen my leg and arm muscles. They were always pleased by how far I could walk using my walker – I put on a good show! However, when at about the eight-year mark I explained that while yes, I could perform the exercises they gave me – they only took about 10 minutes a day - afterward I would have to spend the rest of the day in bed, they told me not to do them anymore.

A key piece of their treatment was that they never did things for me without me asking for assistance. They didn't try to anticipate what I would need ahead of time, or rush ahead of me to prepare to catch me when I fell. I recognized this as a measure of respect and it actually lowered my stress level while doing the exercises.

Years later an Occupational therapist came after I moved into my handicap-accessible apartment and offered excellent tips to minimize the amount of energy I use doing some very basic things. After she evaluated how I moved and did things, she offered very practical solutions and devices to minimize moves and reduce risks. All her ideas were based on her understanding of how muscles work in the human body and the limits my disease placed on mine. I need to stress that she accepted me as I was and understood when I explained how I lived day-to-day. There was no judgment, no condemnation, no if only's. The fact that professionals who deal with disabilities all the time accepted me helped me dismiss the occasional layperson offering comments full of slight condemnations, but there was more.

Some of my family members took it upon themselves to anticipate my needs, out of love and concern. I found myself frustrated by their attitudes and movements, however, but I couldn't identify why. The interactions with the professionals helped clarify my discomfort with my family – I was physically diminished, but really NOT mentally so. I realized everything worked better when I stated my needs before others were "prepared for a fall." I appreciated their love-filled thinking, but I needed the respect garnered by running my show myself.

Now, that was my reaction to people's anticipatory actions – let's talk a minute about the other end of the spectrum: the disabled person who expects everyone to know just what he needs automatically! It is highly unfair to think that a layperson should be naturally fully informed on the needs of another adult. Nor is it the person's responsibility to know. It's as though some newly disabled people revert to their infant personalities, throwing rattles from their high chairs for the joy of watching Mommy give it back to them. That thinking is extremely unhealthy and unfair. For more information on it, read Melody Beatty's "Codependent No More."

Another reaction common to the disabled is the need to control other people's attempts to help, to the extreme. "Open that window for me. No, not that far, just a little. Well, more than that. Oh, just forget it." Or, "Go and get me more batteries for my light. They have to be XYZ brand, those last longer." And when the helper returns with the batteries requested, the response is "You got the wrong kind. Don't you listen? Maybe you should have written it down. I'll try these, but I'll have to find someone who can get the right brand."

There's a lot of discovery when a person becomes disabled. It will bring out the worst in a person due to the anger and frustration caused by it. I maintain, however, that it remains our responsibility to be the best example of Christ we can be; regardless.

I have found it is easiest, when I am with other people, to give them some guidelines before big movements, like getting me into and out of a car, come up. I have also, many times appreciated when I tell someone what I'm planning to do and they offer an easier alternative.

My next step was to look into the Multiple Sclerosis non-profit organizations. I found that the Multiple Sclerosis Association of America (www.mymsaa.org) offered access to practical help as well as cooling devices and support equipment! They even connected me to a resource to help me recoup the money for my Medicare payments for a number of years. Again, in speaking with their representatives, there was no judgment regarding any assistance I needed, and if they couldn't provide the help I was wanting, they at least provided other resources I might try.

Calls to different agencies in my area made it clear that free in-home help was unavailable, which was frustrating. Additionally, as I was under the age of 55, my family and I learned that I didn't qualify for help getting into a handicap-accessible apartment – in other words – my disability happened before anyone was ready to help me live where I would be safer. I later learned that the waiting lists for such units were up to 10 years long in my area! I was frustrated and infuriated all over again! In short, I learned if you're going to become disabled before you're 55, be independently wealthy so you can pay for the help you're going to need, and can build or buy your own handicap-ready living space.

I did eventually get some assistance with food preparation through an organization that reaches out to churches in my area. These two dynamic ladies came once every two weeks to prepare the foods I had always made for myself – using my recipes and methods. They were such a blessing, providing friendship and a sense of continuity. I was eventually able to once again cook for myself, but they were key to my stabilization in those early days of disability.

The Christian counselor I had been seeing for years offered to come to my home, and boy did I need her! She continues to be a safe place to examine what's happened and my feelings about it all. One of the first things I grappled with was accepting that it was okay to feel the way I did, even "bad" feelings. Over the years, Anita has led me along a path of self-acceptance, something I never permitted before. One of the most profound things for me in this journey was realizing that if, as the song says, I am "precious in His sight," that meant I was more than acceptable to Him. This was eye-opening to me, and it lead to the thought "If I'm precious to God, who am I to think I'm a failure or not good enough to myself?" Humbling, but extraordinarily helpful.

So now, ten years into being disabled, I have a helper who comes once a week to help clean, do my laundry, and do anything else I ask of her, including food preparation. I have assistive equipment in my bathroom, bedroom, and kitchen, I still use a walker for tight spots in my home, I have a power wheelchair I use daily, and a manual chair I use if a friend or family member takes me somewhere in their vehicle. I have the confidence to search for assistance as I need it, and the knowledge of where to look for it. I also have the assurance of God's love and caring friends and family willing, to be frank with me AND lend assistance when asked.

FOR YOUR CONSIDERATION

Have you ever had the experience of learning that, in fact, the way you handled things was nothing like the way other people did?

Have you reached out for assistance in your community? Was the result positive, negative, or lukewarm? How did you feel about the result, and why?

Does the condition with which you live have a national non-profit organization, and if so, have you reached out to it for help?

You are precious in His sight; bask in that truth for a minute. What words come to mind regarding it – anger, peace, relief, acceptance, resolve?

What actions will you take now or in the future about requesting assistance?

8. Consider the Listener

I Need to Consider with Whom I Burden with My Truths

Then Jesus said to him, See that you don't tell anyone... *Matthew 8:4*

Then he ordered his disciples not to tell anyone... Matthew 16:20

The purposes for Jesus telling the healed blind man, then later his disciples not to tell what he'd done nor who he was were very different from why we, as disabled people, have to be careful with whom we share our truths. However, just as Jesus was wise in his requests, it is wise for us to use discretion when sharing our experiences.

Loneliness, pain, frustrations, and disappointments are part of everyday life for us, and it's natural for us to need to share these things with others. We can also, out of loneliness, share information that is unsuitable for public discussion. As an example, I was recently having coffee with a group of neighbors when another resident joined us. His conversation included how the food he ate during his recent hospital stay had "plugged him up for four days" and how brutal the constipation, then the voiding, had been. Inappropriate to the max for sure, but I think it was more the result of his need to verbally process his difficulties. I have found there can be intense loneliness even when I am with people.

Some people are just not the right sounding boards. While I find the workings of the human body fascinating and want to learn all I can about what's happening in my body, I have family members who are very squeamish about such things. We need to respect others' comfort levels and cannot assume (as I often have) that everyone has the same interests in the details of our experiences.

51

Then there are people like my sweet mother, who try to take on the responsibility of "fixing" the situation, a futile exercise that drastically increases her personal stress. I've learned over the years to be gentle and mellow when discussing my health. And believe it or not, I've had friends that have had similar reactions to my truths.

And we've already discussed the folks that offer lay-person opinions as to the causes or cures for an affliction. It can be extremely frustrating to share things about our lives with these well-meaning people, not only because their ideas are kind of insulting, but also because they usually can't show the empathy we may be seeking. On top of that, we have to spend time reassuring ourselves that we did nothing to cause our conditions, if we didn't, or forgiving ourselves (perhaps again) if we did.

I have also had the experience of telling a sweet, interested person about my condition – nothing too detailed or personal – but information, only to learn that she prided herself on knowing things about people. Now, I've always been open about having MS, but she made a point of telling anyone and everyone that I had it. That didn't sit well with me, and I finally realized it was because she "outed me," telling people things about me for her own purposes. So be careful around people who gossip.

We always need to consider our audience. Children, even teenagers who act like they know it all, are really not mature enough to handle our trials. I recall when I went partially blind in one eye – the event that solidified my diagnosis – I did my best not to let my preteen son know about it. Once I had the MS diagnosis, my son overheard a phone conversation and flat-out asked if I was going blind. I told him "apparently not in both eyes at the same time," and proceeded to explain my diagnosis in light terms.

In summary, I have learned to consider how sharing my truths with others might impact me, frankly. I am unable to tolerate the additional drama associated with opening up to the wrong people. That sounds harsh, but we have a responsibility to ourselves to minimize our stress! And we still need to process what is happening to us.

Humans verbally process traumatic events. We just do. It is a way for us to try to grasp this weird thing that has happened. It's NORMAL. I once took claims for an insurance company, and could always tell when a customer was still at the scene of an accident because rather than answering my questions, they would repeat, over and over again, everything that happened leading up to and following the event. Becoming disabled is traumatic - perhaps I've said this before. We need to get a handle on it, but I've just said it's not okay to sort it out with the people we might come across, or even our family members! This is where professional counseling comes in.

The safest way to deal with feelings is with a licensed counselor. I know I've spoken of mine before, but considering where to share truths, counseling is the way to go. I think we have progressed past the notion that seeking counseling is a sign of weakness or mental illness or a failure of some sort, as it was seen in the 60s and 70's. Counseling is just a way of sorting out emotions and devising helpful ways to move forward. You can say anything to a counselor, aside from confessing a crime, and it will stay private. Everything from rants to tears - they're ready for it and won't think less of you for it. And if your disability has you isolated like mine does, counseling enables you to speak of other things when you are with people.

There is another source of verbal relief, and that is someone who has your same affliction, who is near the same stage as you. I have so appreciated talking with other people who live with MS. My MS buddies validate my feelings and I do theirs. I can share frustrations and experiences - and they've likely experienced the same things! It is very close to being family - we all speak the same language - and with MS, sometimes our language is gobbledy-gook! It is a wonderful support network, and I love them all.

There is another aspect to considering with whom I burden my truths, and that is not being open to folks with the need to know. As an example, my dad used to tell me about physical problems he was having as we were going to see his doctor, then tell the doctor nothing about them! It was as if he didn't want to burden the doctor, cause a problem, or, more probably, admit to a weakness.

Let's make this clear: You, through your insurance, PAY your medical professionals. They are your employees, if you will, and if you don't communicate what needs to be addressed, things can't be improved! They need input from you to really understand what they need to do, and putting on a happy face doesn't cut it. You need better, you are worthy of better. I have often heard people complain that some ailment was ignored by their doctor, but when I ask straight out if they had told the doctor the way they told me, they say things like "well, they should just know!" They're doctors, not psychics, folks. Spell it out for them - even if you don't have the "right" terms for things. Explain it the best you can, and see what the doctor can do.

This same principle applies to aides, caregivers, and the like. If, when you're alone you lose track of time staring at a cobweb in the corner of your room, but don't mention it to the person who cleans for you, you could watch that thing grow for months! Same goes if you need a box down from up high in your closet. People can only help you most when you kindly express your needs. If you make demands or nasty comments, you'll likely blow through helpers like Sherman did through Georgia in the Civil War. Make a list of things you need, and relay those needs to those who are there to help.

One last thing on sharing: Being honest with yourself. In my situation, there will likely come a time when I should no longer live on my own. This is a truth for which I need to prepare. Though I am weeks from being sixty, I still like to think this is fifteen or twenty years away, but I have no certainty that it will be. So I have a responsibility to identify what behaviors or signs will indicate that it's time for changes to occur. At one point I might have thought repeated falls would be that sign, but then I got my wheelchair. There are times when I'm unable to make food, but I can nuke something or order out. I don't FORGET to eat - to me, that would be a sign. Things I watch for include remembering things, the ability to do basic things like bathing, and the use of my hands and arms. I may have mentioned before that I'm stubborn and a little rebellious, so I'd prefer to have a say in when my needs change, and not wait for someone else to decide that for me. As this is my life, it's my responsibility. And responsibility brings empowerment.

So I will purchase one of those "What to do When I'm Gone" books, and map out my preferences for Long Term Care facilities, things I will need when I go there, and how to handle my belongings. Well before that, however, I will make clear to my family members the things that are signs to me, and clarify that the decision to move will be mine, as long as I'm mentally competent.

Sharing our truths is really about tone, timing, and content. We choose the right tone - whether we need to be gentle or can be blatant, considering our audience; we choose the time to share, based on the audience; and we choose the content, again, considering the audience. By our choosing these things carefully, we have empowerment.

FOR YOUR CONSIDERATION

How deeply has loneliness affected you?

Have you had negative experiences sharing with someone? Was it their fault, or yours?

Have you ever "soft peddled" your reality to a medical pro or caregiver? Will you continue to do so?

What might your future look like? What steps might you take to identify when things need to change?

9. Handling the Comments

But Susan, how do I Handle the Comments?

Oh, the comments! I've already shared some of the comments I've experienced since learning I had MS – the scary, the inconsiderate, the judgmental, the uninformed – they have all come my way over the years. Infuriating. But again, what is my goal? Shining the Light of Jesus isn't going to happen if I permit Susan-the-person to respond the way she wants. Insert expletive here.

In my particular situation, living with MS, I've "enjoyed" people who felt the need to tell me stories of people they've known who had MS – everything from "She's had it for years and you'd never know, except for..." to "And he died from it!" I don't doubt any of them – MS hits every person differently. It is nice to know that I don't have the type that kills, though I used to babysit for a sweet lady that did. But others have jumped to the conclusion when I'm still in the middle of the book, automatically telling me I need to take this extreme step immediately because it's only going to get worse. Or they perceive that I'm already in a worse state of disability than I really am and that I'm deceiving myself. It is insulting, but it still tends to erode my confidence.

I've already mentioned the person who, upon hearing I had MS, chased after me and told me to "Go off Gluten! It will change EVERYTHING!" Frankly, she freaked me out so much that it was years before I discovered the benefits of being gluten-free. But I've also had people telling me to get rid of the fillings in my mouth because they're toxic and to bathe in seaweed for its detoxifying properties. And then all the folks who wanted me to "boost my immune system for protection" were unaware that my immune system is the very thing that is attacking me.

The thing is, these people honestly wanted to help. Or, they

56

were trying to show they knew something about my disease in order to be sympathetic. Do they deserve my biting reaction? Probably not, so what do I do?

First, I always consider the source. Who is speaking? Is this a medical professional, a family member, a friend, or just someone in a group of people? I weigh the comment against who is saying it, and judge from that how much I should consider what was said. To me, the medical professional is always given the most credence, while comments from a family member tend to hurt the most. If it's a friend or a stranger, obviously it doesn't impact me that much.

Then I consider the speaker's motivation. Do they want to share vital information? Are they feeling guilty or recognizing a lack of control? Are they trying to relate to me? Are they the kind of person who needs to demonstrate their knowledge to feel important? Or, are they purposely trying to scare me? I have never come across a person attempting to do the latter – the motives I've determined are all more about the speaker than they are about me. To me, that means I should respond to them respectfully. I can share information with them, or express interest in what they say, and let their comments roll off my back.

Not that my ability to do so was a natural thing. After a few uncomfortable interactions with virtual strangers, I made a plan so I could handle them the way I want to. It reminded me of the coaching parents received in the early 90's – to think through possible conversations with troubled teenagers BEFORE they happened so that the parents would be prepared when and if they did. I list them here in "I will" form because they are powerful that way.

I. I will try to anticipate possible comments so as not to be blindsided when they come up
II. I will decide ahead of time to respond to comments with grace and respect
III. I will respect why they interpret things the way they do – be it guilt, fear, or lack of information
IV. I will respond with my truths without accusations and anger
V. I will ask my medical professional to clarify/determine my needs and act accordingly based on their response

   a.   Doctor agrees with my point of view? I will assure my loved ones

   b.   Doctor agrees with their point of view? I will ask for help to make the changes I need to make

This is one way you can openly and honestly control your reactions to scary conversations, and respond with respect and love. It's good to be prepared for those random interactions, but I've found that they are also effective when facing an uncomfortable interaction with your family.

Nothing erodes my confidence more than when a family member questions my ability to function. The last time it happened, it took me *days* to regain my footing so I could take a long look at my "I will" list and respond appropriately. If I *haven't* said it before, I strive to be a realist about myself – denial and illusions about myself are not part of my successful coping plan. So when it is suggested by a family member that in fact I am NOT fully comprehending my situation, I take a good hard look at my facts. In this last case, I was able to present the facts and give some information that they had lacked when coming to their conclusions. My goal is to recognize my inabilities and responsibly act on them BEFORE anyone else does.

FOR YOUR CONSIDERATION

Have you had a family member suggest you are less than you think you are?

What is your biggest fear regarding the physical losses you might face?

What is the strangest thing anyone has said to you regarding your situation?

Are you the person who "shrugs off" comments, only to have them haunt you in quiet moments? Could the "I will" list quiet those nasty after-thoughts?

10. Let's Talk About Grace

Grace is a multi-faceted thing that is key to accepting a new undesirable way of life. There is God's grace, freely available to every one of us, at any time, unearned and undeserved. Then there's the grace given by others, also freely. This is everything from a stranger holding a door for someone to dinners prepared a delivered to the sick and infirm.

I will admit that accepting grace from others was hard for me once I became disabled. I've addressed how acknowledging the need for assistance is the opposite of how we're brought up in our culture, and how it is an affront to a person's identity of capable independence. And, I'll say it, I had my PRIDE, you know. After turning away offers for assistance a time or two, I came to realize that was kind of stupid since I couldn't do the things an able-bodied person would accomplish in minutes. Too, I remembered that accepting help offered by someone else was allowing them to be a blessing, just as I had been a blessing back when I helped someone. It is worth it to quickly trounce our negative thoughts about needing help in our new norm so we can embrace and freely receive the love and generosity offered.

Once fully accepted, grace from others is shocking, humbling, warm, and powerfully meaningful. Receiving the grace offered by others is a conscious choice that, once made, offers immeasurable blessings. But choosing to fully accept it is always on us. We must choose to accept the grace offered to us by others in part by choosing to ignore the imperfections and limitations of those people, and not asking for more than they can give. Do you see how accepting the grace offered by others includes giving grace too?

A couple of years ago I befriended a neighbor of mine whose outlook was just nasty. Her cup wasn't half full, it was a tacky plastic cup overflowing with all the horrible things that had happened to her in life, including that her cup was only cheap plastic! I thought if she knew she had a friend her life might be better. But you know what? Nothing I ever did for her was good enough. I made a special trip to the store when I really didn't have the energy to get the batteries she needed, but they were the wrong brand. Another time I bought the kind of donuts she liked, but they were obviously not fresh. The last straw for me was when I went to her place to help her with something and she launched into a diatribe about how my wheelchair had run over the shoes she had by the door and didn't I know what fine quality they were? I had to accept that she was stuck in the Anger phase of her grief over multiple life troubles, and she was fine with that. She didn't have any grace to recognize the gifts of grace I had chosen to offer her. So let's shift our focus to the grace *we* might need to practice *giving*.

I've spoken of dealing with people who offer information or "solutions" regarding my illness, and how I work to respond kindly to them. I choose to give them a form of grace; understanding their motivations (usually to support and help) and validating them. I have received gifts of groceries at different times, people bringing items I can "just" whip together for a meal, when in fact, I don't have the energy or functionality to prepare food. I graciously accept these gifts, never mentioning my limitations in favor of absorbing the love represented in the act. It is the act that matters after all. I remain in control over with whom I share my limitations, and I choose to share that information in a way that is loving and clarifying rather than damning. Again, no one can guess what I live with day-to-day, and I don't need to try to make anyone understand. I liken my situation to what I encountered when I had a baby and got comments from non-parents about what they were going to be like when they had children, suggesting I was doing it wrong. Essentially, our ability to understand that others have no concept of our daily lives is key to giving them the grace to accept their well-intended ideas and not engage in further conversation.

I try to be the most gracious about people who go to the trouble of picking me up and taking me places. These folks commit to coming to get me, which adds at least 15 minutes to their travel time, then come in to get me as I can't operate my manual wheelchair long enough to get myself to their vehicle, then they have to collapse the chair and lift it into their car for use when we arrive at our destination! This is no easy commitment on their part.

In these instances, I count it as my responsibility to be fully prepared upon their arrival, which beyond being dressed includes having my supply bag and anything else I'm bringing ready to go, and opening and getting into my manual chair. My preparation includes considering my potential needs while I'm out, including rain gear or a lap blanket to keep my legs warm. Whatever the need, it's my responsibility to have it ready to go when they get here for me. This is a way I can show my gratitude for their gift of time, energy, and consideration.

Another way I can give grace to helpers is to leave them to do whatever tasks they've agreed to do for me. As a control freak, I am naturally frustrated that I can't do things as I once could, so I found that if I stick around to watch the work being done, I'm quickly fighting the urge to "give tips" or "offer helpful ways" to do the task. The people helping me aren't children; they know how to do whatever they're doing! My suggestions or tips are insulting! So I identify the task, provide the necessary supplies for the task, make sure they know I'm available for any questions, and remove myself from the room. I also try hard to no longer give driving tips. I haven't driven in ten years, and roads have changed quite a bit. Additionally, the one that's driving knows how they want to go about it. But man it feels good when they ask for help!

By far, the most important use of grace is giving grace *to yourself.*

    a. Giving it to myself means accepting my own limitations and refusing to punish myself for things I can no longer do

    b. Giving it to myself helps clear the way to identifying those things I can do, and do them well.

I was forced to acknowledge my disability on June 21, 2011.

MS had taken almost everything from me – my ability to drive, to walk, to work, to even think, was gone. In reality, these losses had been a fact of my life for almost ten years already, but I pushed myself to keep trying, largely because the government told me I wasn't disabled enough. Still, acknowledging the truth was devastating. It meant the death of dreams, the loss of income, and a complete change of my life. My sister-in-love took me to the local Social Security office to get the disability paperwork started and she had to answer most of the lady's questions because I couldn't think to answer myself. My mother took over my bills because I couldn't function to pay them. Therapists came into my home with a walker and a wheelchair for MY use! All I could think was "WHAT?!"

I slowly regained my footing and was able to move forward on this new journey, but so much of my energy was spent learning about my new self – what I could do, and what I couldn't. I knew I had to grieve my losses; I had memorized the stages of grief in college – DABDA – Denial, Anger, Bargaining, Depression, and, finally, Acceptance. The goal of grieving is Acceptance.

The grieving process is slow and hard. Even after you feel you've reached acceptance it will wax and wane. But again, acceptance is the **goal**. I'm a very goal-oriented person and was frustrated that I couldn't just skip over Denial, Anger, Bargaining, and Depression to get on with it. Additionally, gaining acceptance is a hard process; it's not something you pick up at the checkout counter with a beef jerky.

It was at least six months before I could manage my own finances again. It took about two years for me to hear God saying "Susan, you still have responsibilities, and the sooner you accept them, the better you'll feel about yourself." I identified and started accepting my new responsibilities, as I could, some with the help of others (wide eye-roll inserted here.) Sure enough, I started feeling grounded, empowered, and yes, much better about myself. At about year three, He downloaded this book into my brain. I should let you know that whenever God downloads to me, it doesn't go away the way my own great ideas do. The outline God downloaded hadn't moved, so I began working on this book. I knew He wanted me to.

Acceptance is also a choice in ANY grief process. A person can choose to learn to live a new life, or they can rale against it, fighting, bitter, angry. But in the latter case, they never move PAST it. Ever. I bet you're thinking about people you know who have never moved on, sadly stuck on any of the grieving stages. I will tell you right now that my faith helped me choose to accept. Some never do, and I wonder if it's because they are unaware they have a choice.

FOR YOUR CONSIDERATION

Have you ever noticed someone exhibiting grace to others? How did you feel about that person?

Have you ever demonstrated grace only to have it misunderstood or rejected? How did you feel about the person who rejected your grace?

After reading this chapter, are you re-examining your reactions to someone's attempt to show you grace? Apologize if you need to.

Has your pride gotten you into trouble the way mine has? Are you ready to put that feeling aside in favor of healthier choices?

Pray that God shows you ways to demonstrate grace to others, every day.

11. Meanwhile...

You do your best to absorb the inevitable changes in your relationships with people. Life continues! People drop out of your sphere – perhaps they still work and move forward in their lives, while yours has, to a large degree, stopped. Everything changes because of our inabilities, and it hurts. For me, the hurt stems from the fact that I'm out-of-step through no fault of my own, and I wish I could still be actively involved. In my dreams I'm always back at my favorite work experience, tasked with making important things happen for the company. I miss the mental exercise of making things happen. It was exhilarating to be respected for my thinking and for what I contributed. The last I heard, one company was still using the words I had written five years after I had left.

I counted myself lucky because I knew that this "distancing" change would happen – maybe through my degree, or out of witnessing it happen to others. When I became disabled, I knew what would happen. The knowledge kept me from being angry at the people I've lost, but it didn't ease the emotional pain one bit.

My disease has added an additional layer of isolation, too. I don't have the energy to talk on the phone for very long, or to interact with groups for hours at a time. And I have no tolerance for loud places – loud actually causes me physical pain. In this current age, restaurants are all about noise at ear-piercing levels – so that people must shout to make themselves heard by a person at the same table. My voice has been weakened by my disease, and it was never boisterous before, so shouting adds more exhaustion to what should be a pleasant time with friends and family. In summary, most restaurants cause me physical pain and add to my exhaustion, all because they think being loud is fun. It isn't.

The change that hurts the most involves my formerly active role in my nuclear family. I was the hands-on helper who made myself available to help my parents whenever I could, especially when my dad was in his last months. I would go over to give my mom a break, cook, or whatever. One of my favorite memories of that precious time was throwing a blanket into the dryer for a few minutes and then spreading it over him – he was unnaturally cold in those days, and the warmed blanket made him smile. Being there was a way for me to show love and respect to both my parents. I had deep, treasured conversations that would only have happened in these situations.

This was a little over two years before my wheels fell off. Since my disability, my mom has been hospitalized three times, and I have been able to visit her once. Now I'm the one getting the calls from my brother after she's been admitted. There is no way I can assist when she is released, either. Ask me how that feels.

God has given me the safe place to dump my anger and pain through all of this. And His word has assured me that He still has plans for me – things for me to do, impacts to make. The world kindly agrees that I can't play its games anymore, but God has, over and again, told me that He's glad my work for Him has finally started. As previously shared, I have done my best to embrace my new life and make positive moves forward. I'd love to tell you I did this out of courage and grit, but really, it was my determination to be my best self while I'm here. And it is hard.

While I was focused on making my new life the best it could be, I still had physical problems that demanded attention. In February of 2019, I learned the Ovarian cancer that had visited me in 1997 had decided to visit again. Boy was I mad! I'm no stranger to surgery and knew very well that the surgery itself is the easy part for me, and I resented the time it would take for me to recover based on all my previous experiences. I had other things planned for the three months I anticipated it would take for me to recover – eating up a significant part of summer! A month after the surgeon told me what and how things would be done, I had the surgery.

This time the tumor was 10 times larger than the first. I lost body parts I didn't know someone could lose in this second cancer surgery. The type of Ovarian cancer I had doesn't respond to chemo or radiation – so all they can do is remove the affected areas. So above recovering from the 9-hour surgery itself, I had to learn to deal with how my body now did what had previously been largely automatic.

After over a week of recovering in the hospital, I was discharged to finish recovering at a nursing home I chose because a friend worked there. The hospital asked again and again if that was where I wanted to go because the place I'd chosen wasn't on their list of approved facilities, but I remained steadfast in support of my friend. That stubborn decision on my part had the angels working overtime to keep me from death – something that would surely have happened due to the negligence of that facility! I truly have never

> Psalm 23:4
> *Even though I walk through the valley of the shadow of death, I will fear no evil, for You are with me; Your rod and Your staff, they comfort me.*

been as afraid for myself as I was there. I was a disabled person recovering from a huge surgery, and I was on my own from the moment I got there. After the required three weeks I was released, and within twenty-four hours I was back in the hospital for another 10 days because of the raging infection (two abscesses) I developed at the home, and that they ignored. I went home with a "pic" line so I could infuse the special drug they had chosen twice a day. With everything my body had endured, combined with the MS that never likes taking second place to something else, when I really felt like a wet "rag" and really couldn't do much for myself.

Still, I am blessed that surgeons were able to remove the tumor and the affected organs completely so that as I write this, I am once again cancer free. The cost of being able to say that, however, was great. My anticipated three-month recovery was highly overly optimistic, it had been eight months by the time I fully recovered from the surgery and the abuses at the nursing home. And, I have been hospitalized about six times since the surgery for problems that will be a part of my life from now on. So yes, other health concerns can pop up in addition to your primary disability.

THE THING IS, God was right there through all of it. Not that I could always feel His presence, but I knew, even at my sickest moments, that I wasn't alone, and that He would see to my healing. I was amazed at how close to death I came, and I certainly didn't appreciate the experiences I had, but I knew I would come out of it alive because He had assured me of it before it all started.

Then there's the other stuff going on that impact our lives! Threats to our way of life have become constant, the concepts of right and wrong change with no notice, inflation impacts how we can live, and we find causes that demand our energy. All while our physical losses become more evident.

However, as long as we have mental capacity, it remains our responsibility to plan for our futures. Planning to die in our sleep before we must rely on the help of others to move, dress, or prepare meals isn't responsible or respectable. Neither is determining to end one's life before things get that bad. So, we need to take a realistic look at our next steps.

You might be thinking "How do I know what's going to happen? I wasn't expecting this!" I'm right there with you, but this isn't about predicting the future, it's about researching options and clearly communicating with family. While it was easy to create a "How to" document to share with my family regarding things to monitor as signs I need more help, I shied away from doing anything more for close to two months out of fear of what I'd learn. Finally, I took it to God – yelling at Him one day because I felt so inadequate. And as is always the case when I do that, I woke the next morning knowing the next step to take – making a couple of phone calls to places that could give me some guidance! It takes some brain stretching – or it did for me, but I reached out to my area's Agency on Aging and to the Social Worker at my GP's office for guidance.

I found articles on how to know if it's time for Assisted Living on the internet, too, and I purchased AND completed a simple Will document so that my son doesn't have to wait for probate when I die. I felt so much better about myself by just making those phone calls! I had stopped listening to fear and a bad attitude and reasserted my power as a functioning Child of God!

Honestly, I have no control over my future. It belongs to God and will be impacted by the progress of my disease. But the last time I had to move, I was unsure of where I could go but having looked, I told God what I preferred, and He made it happen in quick order. Knowing my options enables me to at least discuss them with God, knowing He will make the perfect thing happen at the appropriate time. Knowing my options includes embracing my financial limitations, too. Once again, by choosing to live in reality, I spare myself the pain of wishing I could move into places I will not be able to afford. It's a waste of time and energy to pretend and hope.

Taking the above steps – looking for options – taking some concrete steps now (making a list identifying the signs things need to change, completing the Will, doing the Power of Attorney) helps me feel less like a flying cannonball, aimed by somebody else and more like a Cattail – secure and strong while sitting in changing waters. And if like the Cattail I can be a little invasive by encouraging you to take the same steps, we'll make a pretty picture!

FOR YOUR CONSIDERATION

Do you miss working? Which part hurts the most for you – the people, conceiving the plan, watching it come together, the satisfaction of success?

Do you find yourself angry over the loss of work, or are you glad those days are done?

Have you found other useful ways to fill your time, or has your physical condition demanded most of it?

Have you felt side-lined, like you're out-of-step with others now that you don't work?

What is your plan for the future? Have you shared it with your family?

12. Ultimately, Responsibility = Empowerment

So what are the messages of this book? First, that every loss of physical ability causes grief, and that to be overcome, we each need to journey through grief to reach acceptance. Acceptance is the goal.

Additionally, as we proceed through the grieving process we can learn to identify things we no longer control as well as things we do still control, like our finances. We might also discover we have responsibilities that are new to us, like some of the things listed in this book. And, also like some topics covered here, we might come to accept that we have greater responsibilities than we had before, like monitoring with whom we share details of our lives.

Accepting your responsibilities as a disabled person takes time, takes brain work and takes grace. It also takes a conscious decision to make the best of your new situation. Not everyone chooses to still strive for their best, and please remember not everyone, especially those with brain damage, *can*.

Striving to accept your new reality provides a sense of self-respect and a sense of peace. Even this many years later, I am still relieved on the days when I need to stay in bed – that I can do it without having to pretend I don't. For so many years I berated myself for being wimpier than other people. The fact of my disability permitted me to respect myself.

And since I live in a northern state, I am also relieved that I don't have to pretend that scraping off my car after working during a snowy day is somehow acceptable – because that became nearly impossible for me to do, trudging through knee-high snowdrifts and pulling snow off windows using a brush that was almost too heavy to lift.

EMPOWERED THOUGH DISABLED

By far though, accepting my new responsibilities as a disabled person EMPOWERED me at a time that I thought I had lost everything that made me who I am. And that has been worth all of it.

Printed in the USA
CPSIA information can be obtained
at www.ICGtesting.com
LVHW071800111123
763676LV00057B/1208